The

DALE CARNEGIE COURSE

in

Effective Speaking
Human Relations

and

Developing Courage and Confidence
Improving Your Memory
Leadership Training

How the Course is Conducted
and
What You Do at Each Session

Twenty-Fifth Edition Copyright ©1960, 1962, 1964, 1966, 1968

DALE CARNEGIE & ASSOCIATES, INC.

Garden City, New York 11530

TABLE OF CONTENTS

TABLE OF CONTENTS (Cont'd)

In the sessions that follow you will find reading assignments based on the three books I wrote to help people express themselves more effectively, get along with others and lead happier lives. They are:

The Quick and Easy Way to Effective Speaking
How to Win Friends and Influence People
How to Stop Worrying and Start Living

If you read the assignments in each of these books faithfully, you will get far greater benefit from the Course, because you will have a clear understanding of the sessions and you will be better able to apply what you learn to your everyday life.

The reading assignments are arranged to prepare you for a successful experience in each session.

In addition to the three volumes listed above, you will be asked to read several booklets in preparation for specific sessions.

I firmly believe that if you read and study these three books and the booklets you will double the benefit you will receive from the Course.

PLEASE BE SURE TO READ
THIS IMPORTANT ADVICE

How to Get the Most Out of This Training
by DALE CARNEGIE

Congratulations on your vision, courage and determination. When you enrolled you showed the will to succeed. Many people have the desire just as you do; they have a wishbone instead of a backbone. But you have determination. Because of it you are embarking on a bold, rewarding and fascinating voyage of self-realization.

When you have completed this training, you will probably be astonished at how much you have gained from it. You will probably have progressed far more than you now dream possible. For the rest of your life, you may look back upon this Course as one of the turning points of your career. Those statements sound like wild exaggerations, don't they? But they are not. They are the sober truth. I know, because I have seen this training work veritable miracles in the lives of ambitious men and women.

Your Attitude is All-Important

Occasionally men and women register for this Course with a lackadaisical attitude which is tantamount to saying, "Here's my enrollment fee. Let's see what you can do for me." If that is your attitude, please do not take this training.

On the other hand, if you say, "I am giving you my enrollment fee; and, in addition, I am going to give you my enthusiastic co-operation; I believe in this training, and I am going after it like a bulldog after a cat." If that is your attitude, we can help you help yourself to an extent that may almost take your breath away.

What You May Expect From This Training

If you would like to know precisely what miracles this training can perform for you, please ask your instructor for a list of the names and addresses of local persons who have taken this Course, and phone or call on them to learn at first hand what they got out of it.

5

One of the most valuable qualities you will develop in this Course is the ability to speak with more poise, more courage and more self-confidence — regardless of whether you are talking to one person or a thousand.

I have written a book entitled *How to Stop Worrying and Start Living*. I have read almost every book written in English on the subjects of fear and worry and I have discussed these subjects with thousands of people. I have been training men and women to develop courage and self-confidence for many years. After all that experience, I can honestly say that, except for religion, if there has ever been devised a better way of conquering fear and developing courage than the training you will receive in this Course, I have never heard of it.

Think Yourself Brave

You have already begun to develop courage. You have already taken a bold and courageous step by enrolling for this Course. So, begin this instant to think of yourself as a person of courage, because, *as you think, so you will be.*

Who is stopping you from being self-confident and self-reliant right now? I am not. Nobody is stopping you but *yourself.*

Having courage does not depend on what is happening outside you. It depends entirely on what is happening inside you. Only thoughts can give you courage, and only thoughts can give you fear. So start right now thinking thoughts of courage.

You Get Many Chances to Talk

I have a much-prized letter from George Bernard Shaw saying that when he was a young man, eager to conquer shyness and timidity and his fear of speaking in public, he attended every meeting in London where there was to be a public discussion and always arose and took part in the debate. He spent almost every

6

other night for twelve years addressing audiences all over England and Scotland. Finally, this young man, who had been too shy and timid to ring the doorbell of his close friends, made himself one of the most brilliant speakers and debaters of his age.

George Bernard Shaw was right. And the Course does exactly as he suggests. It gives you many opportunities to speak. As a result, you will take a more active part in talks and discussions in your business and your community.

Get Busy and Fear Will Vanish

Afraid? Go right on in spite of your fear — and your fear will begin to vanish. That is the advice that was given to me by General A. A. Vandegrift when he was head of the United States Marine Corps. I asked him if soldiers were afraid when they were going into battle with bullets whistling by and shells bursting all around them. He replied, "Any man who says he isn't afraid under those conditions is either lying or weak-minded; but the thing to do in battle is to go right on. Keep busy and ignore your fears, and they will vanish." General Vandegrift told me that his favorite motto is "God favors the bold and strong of heart." Why not make that your motto too? *God favors the bold and strong of heart.*

This Training Will Help You Talk to Large Groups

You may ask, "Will this training help me when I have to talk to large groups?" Of course it will!! What is a large audience except a lot of individuals? Never worry about the size of your audience — talk to ten thousand in the same conversational manner you use in talking to an individual. Have the right subject for *YOU*, plus an eager desire to talk about it, and you can be effective before ten thousand listeners.

How This Course Is Conducted

Your class meets one evening each week for fourteen weeks. Each session lasts approximately four hours and is divided into two parts — A and B. You speak two or more times each evening.

Because you have so many chances to speak and because of the helpful suggestions you receive from your instructors, you make rapid progress in building poise and self-confidence — *you learn to speak by speaking*.

If you are compelled to miss any sessions, you are urged to make them up in current classes or in future classes, or even in other cities, without any additional cost. If it should be necessary to make up a session in another city, the person who offers the Course in your area, or your instructor, will provide you with a letter of authorization.

Your Instructors Are Especially Trained

The instructors of The Dale Carnegie Course come from Speech and English departments of leading universities, from executive and managerial positions in the business world, from the pulpit, from the lecture platform and other professional positions. Regardless of their background they are required to go through an intensive training program and to attend a refresher clinic every year. The instructors will tell you what is right with your talk and show you how it may be improved. They will tell you how to select subjects you have earned the right to talk about, how to make your talks interesting, how to give them audience impact. They will help you learn to use the Magic Formula and to improve your delivery. They will also help you with human relations problems.

The Graduate Assistants Will Help You

The graduate assistants are outstanding members of previous classes who have been selected to take the Dale Carnegie graduate assistant training program. They are especially trained to be of service to you. They are not paid for their services. Their compensation is the pleasure and satisfaction of seeing you progress toward your goals.

These trained assistants help you to gain courage and self-confidence, to become more effective speakers and to apply the rules for winning friends and influencing people. They are available to counsel with you as friends, to help you over the rough spots and to bring you through the Course triumphantly.

Awards at Most Sessions

In some sessions, books are awarded. In other sessions the awards are appropriately inscribed pencils.

Please Bring This Book to Each Session

In the following pages you will find a description of all sessions of the Course. These sessions will be taught in the order in which they appear in this book. The reading and speaking assignments for Part A and Part B of each session are listed below the title of each session.

Do Not Worry About Accents

If you have an accent, please remember that a slight accent is often an asset. It frequently gives distinction to a man and charm to a woman.

Basis on Which Diplomas Are Awarded

In order to obtain a diploma in this Course, you must: (a) have attended a minimum of 11 of the 14 scheduled classroom sessions, (b) be declared by your instructor (or instructors) and graduate assistants as having made progress worthy of the award of a diploma and (c) have completed payment of your tuition fees.

Facsimile of the diploma you will receive at the end of the Course, provided you fulfill the conditions outlined on Page 9 of this book. Resolve now to be a proud recipient of this certificate.

Dale Carnegie Course

This certifies that

has successfully completed the
Dale Carnegie Course
in Effective Speaking
and Human Relations

In Witness Whereof, this certificate
is issued under our hands and seal
this   day of

Dorothy Carnegie

Session 1

A—How to Remember Names

B—Developing Courage

A—HOW TO REMEMBER NAMES

Tonight you will have an opportunity to get acquainted with the other members of your class and to learn their names.

To give you an incentive and also an opportunity to learn these names, a "Name Exercise" will be staged. No preparation is needed, no formal talks, nothing to do but settle back, have a good time and perhaps answer some questions about yourself and see how many names you can remember. No harm if you don't remember any — but of course you will try to remember the most! You will also learn an easy way to remember a series of objects or items by the "stacking" technique.

Visitors Are Welcome at This Session

Do you have a friend who could profit by taking this Course? If so, why not bring him* as a guest to this session?

B—DEVELOPING COURAGE

Assignments

Reading: *The Quick and Easy Way to Effective Speaking,* Chapter 1 — "Acquiring the Basic Skills."

Speaking: Talk about yourself by answering some of the questions on Page 12.

---

*Throughout this book we say "he," "him," "the man," and "the men." Quite obviously, in almost every case, we mean "the man or woman," "the men or women," and "he or she."

11

You will be asked to talk about yourself for not more than two minutes. Easy? Yes, talking about yourself is far from difficult. It is almost second nature.

Don't bother to make a speech — just answer the questions below. You won't even have to stand when you talk. You and several other class members will be called to the front of the room at the same time. You will sit together on top of a long table facing the class. Relax and tell us about yourself and your reasons for taking this Course.

Please answer the following questions and, remember, your instructor will be standing by to help you.

1. **What is your name?**

2. **Where do you live?**

3. **Where do you work?**

4. **What kind of work do you do?** Are you a Salesman? Household executive? Engineer? Secretary?

5. **How did you hear about this Course?** From a graduate? A class member? If so, how did the Course help him? A relative? A friend? Your employer? What did he say?

6. **What do you hope to get out of this training?**

   (a) Do you expect to use this training in your work, business or profession? How?

   (b) Do you want to be able to think on your feet and to express yourself before groups? Where? How may it help you?

   (c) Do you wish to learn more about how to win friends and influence people? Why?

All Members Are Allowed Equal Speaking Time

In Part B of each session, talks will be limited to two minutes unless otherwise specified. A graduate assistant will start a stopwatch with the first word of your talk. If you are still speaking at the end of the allotted time, he will ring a bell. You must stop talking the instant the bell rings. My experience of many years has taught me that this two-minute rule will help you develop the ability to put your talk across briefly — to make your complete talk in two minutes.

In the Early Sessions You Will NOT Be Told About Your Speaking Faults

Certain ambitious or impatient class members feel that they should be told about their faults at once. I tried that system long ago and discarded it. I found by long experience that telling a nervous, excited individual, a man blinded by fear, that he didn't half open his mouth, that he couldn't be heard in the back of the room, that he said "jist," that he failed to make his point, that he lacked enthusiasm — I found that such criticism terrified him and did more harm than good.

Pay Attention to All Comments

Your instructor will make helpful comments, so please pay attention to them. You will learn not only from the suggestions regarding your own talks, but quite as much from those the instructor makes on the talks of others. You may wish to keep a record of these comments in the blank space provided at the end of each session.

13

How to Get the Most Out of This Course

What you get out of this training depends almost entirely upon what you put into it. This is true not only of this training, but also of all education and of life. Doctor A. Lawrence Lowell, former President of Harvard University, said:

> "There is only one thing that will train the human mind and that is the voluntary use of the mind by the man himself. You may aid him, you may guide him, you may suggest to him and above all else you may inspire him; but the only thing worth having is that which he gets by his own exertions, and what he gets is in direct proportion to what he puts into it."

Make Notes on Ideas for Talks

As various ideas come to you regarding your speaking assignments, write them down. You will find a work sheet for this purpose at the end of the outline for each session. On the way home from tonight's session, I strongly urge you to begin thinking about your topic for next week's talk and to jot down any ideas that occur to you.

Name of Instructor Tonight_____

Comments by Instructor:

Notes for My Talk at the Next Session:

Part B: A Childhood Incident

Session 2

A—Remembering Made Easy
B—Developing Poise and Self-Confidence

A—REMEMBERING MADE EASY

Assignments

Reading: *The Quick and Easy Way to Effective Speaking*, review Chapter 1 — "Acquiring the Basic Skills." *How to Stop Worrying and Start Living*, Part I — "Fundamental Facts You Should Know About Worry."

Memory: Memory Pegs 1 through 10.

Tonight you will learn more about memory. You will be excited and thrilled with the technique your instructor will teach you. With this technique you will be able to remember a list of objects, a grocery list, the points of a talk or a presentation and many other things. In preparing for this session, please memorize the following "memory peg" words:

One	—	**Run**
Two	—	**Zoo**
Three	—	**Tree**
Four	—	**Door**
Five	—	**Hive**
Six	—	**Sick**
Seven	—	**Heaven**
Eight	—	**Gate**
Nine	—	**Wine**
Ten	—	**Den**

You will also be taught how to memorize rules. Your instructor will show you how to apply the peg method to remembering the first nine rules of human relations. In this way you will take the first step toward applying these rules in your daily life. Thus you will be able in 6B to report on an incident involving your experience in using a rule.

B—DEVELOPING POISE AND SELF-CONFIDENCE

Assignments and Awards

Reading: *The Quick and Easy Way to Effective Speaking,* Chapter 2 — "Developing Confidence."
How to Win Friends and Influence People, Part I — "Fundamental Techniques in Handling People."

Speaking: Two minutes — Talk about *one* incident out of your childhood.

Awards: **Best Speech, Most Improvement and Special Award pencils.**

To find a subject to talk about tonight, look back over your childhood and select an event that stands out in your memory. This will be easy to talk about. What is it? Your most memorable Christmas? Your first bicycle? Your childhood sweetheart? An incident in school? The day you skipped school? The time you told a lie? The day you learned to swim?

How to Prepare This Talk

Select at once the incident you are going to talk about and discuss it at every opportunity this week with your friends. These informal discussions will help you when you give your talk.

Do NOT attempt to cover too many ideas in your talk. If you do, it will be too sketchy. Instead, limit your self to ONE incident.

17

The whole purpose of this talk is to give you experience which will develop your confidence in speaking before groups.

Do not write out what you are going to say. Above all, do not memorize it word for word. That procedure almost always proves to be disastrous. Don't even think about making a talk. Merely chat with us for two minutes about your experiences in the same spontaneous, natural way you would talk to a person across the dinner table.

Tonight You Get the Secrets of Successful Speaking

Before you leave tonight you will receive a booklet I wrote, entitled *A Quick and Easy Way to Learn to Speak in Public.* This is *the most important booklet in the Course.* It reveals the secrets of effective speaking that took me years to discover. I have tried to tell you these secrets simply and clearly and to illustrate them vividly. I urge you to carry this booklet with you and to read it at least three times next week. Read it; study it; underscore the vital parts. Make it your guidebook in this Course!

Tonight you learned how to peg the first nine rules from *How to Win Friends and Influence People.* This is more than a Course in Public Speaking — it is designed to help develop the ability to get along with others.

Begin now to put these nine rules into practice. You will be amazed at the difference it will make in your life.

You will be eager, then, to inspire the class to use these rules by your talk in Session 6 in which you will give a specific incident of how you applied one of the rules and what happened when you did.

Name of Instructor Tonight_____

Comments by Instructor:

Notes for My Talks at the Next Session:

Part A: An Incident Involving an Exhibit

Part B: An Unforgettable Experience That I am Eager to Share With My Class

Session 3

A—How to Seize and Hold Attention
B—A Quick and Easy Way to Learn to Speak in Public

A—HOW TO SEIZE AND HOLD ATTENTION

Assignments

Reading: *How to Stop Worrying and Start Living*, Part II — "Basic Techniques in Analyzing Worry."

Speaking: Ninety seconds — Talk about an incident in your life using an exhibit to illustrate your experience.

Enliven Your Talk with an Exhibit

Please bring to class tonight an article or piece of equipment, something connected with an incident in your life about which you can talk for ninety seconds.

A visual aid has these advantages:

1. Your exhibit will help you get your mind off yourself and put you more at ease.
2. It will aid you in making your talk clearer and more vivid. An exhibit is worth a thousand words of description.
3. It will enable you to seize and hold attention. An exhibit makes a talk more interesting.

Here are Five Simple Rules on the Use of Exhibits

1. Pick up your exhibit only when you are ready to use it.
2. Hold your exhibit high enough so all may see it.
3. Hold your exhibit so it does not hide your face.

4. Talk to the audience, not to the exhibit.

5. When you are finished with your exhibit, put it aside.

Years ago, a class member who ran a linotype machine for a newspaper brought as exhibits slugs of metal type that he had made with his machine. I still remember the talk because of the exhibits.

I also remember the talk a class member made twenty-five years ago. He used exhibits in every talk he made. The night he told an incident about his hobby of collecting harmless snakes, he brought three specimens to class in a sack. One got loose and wriggled around the room. I still remember that talk twenty-five years after I heard it — and probably so does everyone who was present!

In Akron, Ohio, a housewife, whose hobby was baking, brought a delicious angelfood cake and told how she had made it that morning. (The class had a party!)

B—A QUICK AND EASY WAY TO LEARN TO SPEAK IN PUBLIC

Assignments and Awards

Reading: *The Quick and Easy Way to Effective Speaking*, Chapter 3 — "Speaking Effectively the Quick and Easy Way."

How to Win Friends and Influence People, Part II — "Six Ways to Make People Like You."

The booklet, *A Quick and Easy Way to Learn to Speak in Public*.

Speaking: Two minutes — Talk about an experience you have lived through and will never forget, one you are eager to tell.

Awards: **Best Speech, Most Improvement and Special Award pencils.**

Last week, you were given my booklet, *A Quick and Easy Way to Learn to Speak in Public.* Let me repeat: in my opinion, it is *the most important booklet in this Course.* It contains little-known secrets of effective speaking.

If this booklet had been in existence when I was in college, I would gladly have walked five hundred miles to get it. I mean that literally. It would have saved me years of struggle, heart-break and futility.

Follow its suggestions. You will soon conquer your fear of speaking, develop a surprising courage and self-confidence and also develop the ability to speak effectively.

A Quick and Easy Way to Learn to Speak in Public **explains why your progress in the Course depends largely on your choosing the right topic for you.**

> *The right topic for you is some experience you have lived through and will never forget — one you are eager to tell us.*

For example, I would be a total failure if I tried to talk on "electronics" or "gold mining in South Africa," because I know nothing about these subjects and care little about them. But I could hardly fail were I to talk about the kind of education I received in college. On that subject I have feelings and convictions I long to convey to you.

Tonight you will talk for two minutes on an incident about which you know you have earned the right to talk. Select an incident about which you feel deeply and are eager to tell us.

Carry These Rules With You

Tonight you will be given a copy of *The Little Golden Book of*

23

Rules which lists the rules from *How to Win Friends and Influence People* and *How to Stop Worrying and Start Living*.

Always carry this booklet and keep applying its rules. You will win more friends, do less worrying and lead a richer and happier life.

Observe These Rules in Preparing Your Talks

Tonight you will also receive my booklet *How to Make Our Listeners Like Us*. Read this booklet before every session, since some of the rules should be applied in every talk you give.

At Session 1, you were given my book, *How to Stop Worrying and Start Living*. Please begin putting the rules of this book into practice in your daily life. If you do, you will lead a happier life. You will also be prepared to make a talk in Session 10, "How to Control Worry and Reduce Tension."

Name of Instructor Tonight_____

Comments by Instructor:

Notes for My Talks at the Next Session:

Part A: An Incident Involving a Lot of Activity

Part B: An Incident in My Life that Taught Me a Lesson

Session 4

A—Expressing Yourself More Naturally
B—How to Make Your Talk Sparkle

A—EXPRESSING YOURSELF MORE NATURALLY

Assignments

Reading: *How to Stop Worrying and Start Living*, Part III — "How to Break the Worry Habit Before it Breaks You," Chapters 6, 7 and 8.

How to Win Friends and Influence People, review Part I — "Fundamental Techniques in Handling People."

Speaking: Ninety seconds — Relate an incident out of your life, demonstrating an activity just as it happened in your experience.

To speak effectively in public or anywhere else, we must use more than just our voice. We must also use physical animation or gestures. In other words, we should use our whole body.

Are gestures important? The canned variety is not. But natural, forceful, spontaneous gestures are extremely important for two reasons:

1. They stimulate and inspire the speaker himself. Gestures wake us up, loosen us up, relax us and get us out of our shells. When we gesture — when we let ourselves go physically — we automatically let ourselves go mentally and emotionally.

2. They also affect the audience. The emotional effect they have on the listeners probably could be measured by instruments.

Before you talk tonight, you will be "introduced" to "The Duke of York." This amusing warm-up will help you to relax and to speak with your body.

How to Augment an Incident with Physical Activity

For your ninety-second talk, select an incident that involves an activity — one that requires physical action — the more energetic the better.

An incident concerned with sports or recreation will usually offer the speaker plenty of opportunity to use physical activity. Try to remember some experience in a game when you made (or missed) the crucial shot, hit the winning home run or struck out. When you give your talk, please tell us what you did and show us animatedly how you did it.

Some Suggested Activities

Here are some incidents which require gestures and bodily action. They would be unnatural and stiff without their innate activity.

1. **Football.** Tell about the time you broke away for your longest run, threw the touchdown pass or kicked the vital goal.

2. **Fishing.** Show us how you hooked and landed that big one.

3. **Skiing.** Tell us how you kept going throughout your most difficult descent — or took your worst spill.

4. **Golf.** Relive for us the time you cracked out your best drive or sliced into the water.

5. **Decorating.** Let us see you when you painted or papered a room or built a new feature for your home. Plenty of action here. Hanging some lovely new curtains works well for the ladies.

6. **Tennis.** Relive that final game of the final set in a match you'll never forget.

7. **Hunting.** When you sighted the deer and what happened as you pulled the trigger.

8. **Changing a tire.** Remember that awful time when your tire blew or went flat.

9. **Gardening.** Plenty of activity incidents here. Or have you forgotten that sore back?

B—HOW TO MAKE YOUR TALK SPARKLE

Assignments and Awards

Reading: *The Quick and Easy Way to Effective Speaking*, Chapter 4 — "Earning the Right to Talk."

The booklets, *How to Make Our Listeners Like Us* and *A Quick and Easy Way to Learn to Speak in Public.*

Speaking: Two minutes — A talk based on an incident out of your life that taught you a lesson. Relive the experience and act it out.

Awards: **Best Speech, Most Improvement and Special Award pencils.**

If you were to ask me to give you one of the most valuable secrets for making a memorable talk, I would say: Use details! What are details? They are specific facts and actions that create a picture in words that enable our listeners to visualize what we are saying. A good speaker never states a few colorless generalities and dull facts; instead, his talk sparkles with interesting details and actions that "paint a picture."

Think how much more interesting a speaker is when he "gets down to cases." Such a talk is not only more vivid, but it is more easily remembered. It is easy to forget *statements* made by a speaker. It is almost impossible to forget a talk rich with specific, clear, interesting *details and actions*. Let me illustrate what I mean:

A Talk Without Details

When I was a kid I grew up on a farm. My older brother used to get me into a lot of trouble. Once he tricked me into upsetting a beehive so that he might rush in and make off with the honey.

He *made off* all right — in the opposite direction — to watch those bees chew me nearly to pieces.

The Same Talk With Details

When my brother Leon and I were kids, we grew up on a farm in North Carolina. Leon was just enough older than I to get me into a peck of trouble. One day as we were tramping through a woods, we spied a beehive. Leon said, "Ken, let's raid that hive and get some honey for Mother."

He picked up a stick about four feet long. As he handed it to me, he said, "Ken, sneak up to the hive and topple it over with this stick — meanwhile I'll get behind that tree over there to rush in and grab the honey when the bees fly away. Mother will be glad to have the honey."

As Leon circled to get behind the tree opposite me, I was happy to think that we were pleasing Mother. When I thought Leon had gone behind the tree, I heard his shout, "Push it over now, Ken." Just as I toppled the hive, I caught a glimpse of Leon streaking up a hill in the opposite direction.

The whole swarm of bees was on me in a moment. They stung my bare feet. They got down into my unbuttoned shirt. They went up the legs of my overalls. Believe me, friends, that was the last beehive I ever trifled with.

Which version of robbing the beehive do you prefer — the short one of bare facts, or the one filled with the colorful, dramatic, and "stinging" details? Incidentally, the second talk was made in a Dale Carnegie class in Norfolk, Virginia.

Let me give you another example. If we say, "It was a narrow escape," we are vague and uninteresting — we could say almost the same of a dozen things that happen to everybody every day. But suppose we say instead, "We found that if we had swerved another three inches to the right, we would have gone over a thousand-foot drop." This could be said truthfully of only one narrow escape in a million! It is factual, explicit and interesting.

Fill Your Talk With Facts and Action

To make your talk sparkle, *please start your talk by answering one of the following questions: Who* was involved? *What* happened? *Where* did it happen? *When* did the incident occur? A speaker, of course, must use judgment, otherwise he may introduce so much detail that his talk will be boring. So don't waste time explaining and setting the scene. Remember, get right down to cases.

Your Assignment For Tonight

Please prepare a two-minute talk based on an incident out of your life *that taught you a lesson.* Answer for us the questions *who, what, where, when, and how,* particularly *what* you did and *how* you did it. **Be sure to relive and even act out the experience.**

Please Review These Booklets

How to Make Our Listeners Like Us

Your talk should afford you an excellent opportunity to use several of the rules from *How to Make Our Listeners Like Us*. Almost all of these rules should be used regularly in conversation except, perhaps, Rules 1 and 11.

A Quick and Easy Way to Learn to Speak in Public

You should find this booklet helpful in preparing any talk you will ever have to make. *A Quick and Easy Way to Learn to Speak in Public* will help you to become a more interesting speaker.

Start Getting Ready for the "Enthusiasm" Session

Tonight you will be given an inspiring booklet entitled *The Little Recognized Secret of Success*. Regardless of whether you are a salesman, a household executive, or an engineer, you can profit by reading *The Little Recognized Secret of Success*. You should read it in order to prepare for your talk at the eighth session.

In Part B of Session 8, you will be asked to tell the class what you gained by using *increased* enthusiasm.

In order to have a successful talk, please begin right now to act *five* times as enthusiastically as you ever have before.

Please remember:

1. When we speak of enthusiasm we are *not* speaking of loudness, shouting or boisterousness. We are speaking of intensity of feeling and the resultant animation. By enthusiasm we mean earnestness and a joyous lifting of the spirit.

2. If, as a result of taking this training, you develop more spirit, more life, and more enthusiasm, you will have a more attractive personality. If you are in business your increased enthusiasm could bring you increased earning power. Yes, real, genuine, heartfelt enthusiasm is one of the little-recognized secrets of success in almost any undertaking.

So start now to renew your interest in your work, yourself and your friends. You can do it if you will only keep thinking about it. Here's a suggestion — paste a note on your mirror: "Act enthusiastic," so you can't help seeing it when you dress. Put similar notes on your desk at the office or on your machine at the shop. Tell your wife what you are doing and ask her to remind you — also your assistant, your secretary, or the gang at the plant or the office.

Some Specific Areas Where Enthusiasm Will Work Wonders

1. Is there an unpleasant chore you have been putting off for a long time? Use enthusiasm and watch how fast it will be accomplished.

2. Are you getting rusty on the job? Resolve to apply enthusiasm to every detail of your job during an entire day. You will be amazed at the results.

3. Do you start your day in low key? Use enthusiasm from the moment you get up and see the difference it will make.

4. Is there an idea you want to sell to your associates, your family, your boss? Use enthusiasm and watch how easily you will get it across.

5. You are practicing human relations rules every day. Resolve to use one rule with all the enthusiasm you can muster. You will see how it will work wonders for you.

Enthusiasm is that ingredient of vitality, mixed with belief in what you are doing, that will insure the success of any project you undertake.

If a class member gained nothing from this training except increased enthusiasm, he would be well paid for his time and effort.

Start now to use more enthusiasm each day, then you will have a story of a *current* application of enthusiasm in your talk at the eighth session.

Select a Topic for the "Coming Out of Your Shell" Session

You should begin at once to select a topic for the "Coming Out of Your Shell" Session next week. If you do not have an incident, please turn to Pages 111 to 117 and you will find two hundred topics for talks. There you can find something that will arouse your fighting spirit.

Take an incident which highlights a subject you are excitedly for or against (an incident you have the right to talk about, one about which you are excited) — think about it all week — talk to your friends about it. Then come to class and "give 'em both barrels" as we used to say back in Missouri. How did it happen? Where did it happen? What effect did it have on you? We are interested in your feelings as well as what you did physically.

WARNING—HAVE ENOUGH MATERIAL: Many class members at the fifth session have only enough material to last perhaps fifteen or twenty seconds. Be sure you have a specific incident to talk about so that you can keep going full-blast for sixty seconds.

PLEASE READ THIS PAGE SEVERAL TIMES

This Course has been conducted since October 22, 1912. In all that time, this training has been developed, tested and improved in the laboratory of experience. So relax. Realize that if you give us your complete cooperation, *together* we shall produce results that may seem miraculous. And they *are* miraculous. In fourteen weeks, if you cooperate, you will probably make more advancement in the development of courage and self-confidence and the ability to deal with people and speak before groups than you have made in the preceding fourteen years. Be patient — and let the miracles happen inside yourself.

Please don't expect those miracles in the first few sessions. They may be happening — but you may not recognize them until later in the Course.

Use the right yardstick in measuring your progress. Don't compare yourself with other speakers in the class. Compare yourself, as the Course progresses, *with yourself at the beginning.*

Do not expect steady, uniform improvement. It does not come steadily — it comes in waves! Perhaps you will improve for two or three sessions, then you will hit a plateau, where you see no improvement for a session or two; you may even appear to slip back for a session or two. Don't let that disturb you. Soon you will again show great improvement. Then you may hit another plateau, another slump, more progress, and so it will go.

Please understand that, in learning an art, a game, or a skill, this uneven progress is normal and natural.

Dale Carnegie

35

Name of Instructor Tonight

Comments by Instructor:

Notes for My Talk at the Next Session:

Part B: An Incident That Made Me Excited

Session 5

A—Thinking on Your Feet
B—Coming Out of Your Shell

A—THINKING ON YOUR FEET

Assignments

Reading: *How to Stop Worrying and Start Living*, Part III — "How to Break the Worry Habit Before It Breaks You," Chapters 9, 10 and 11.

Memory: The words of the "Box Factory" (see below).

Speaking: Sixty-second impromptu talk. No preparation.

Before your talk tonight, you will participate in an action-packed incident which is designed to help you let go freely with your entire body. You will use gestures, and you will enjoy using them. In preparation for this event, please memorize the following incident about a visit to a box factory. Concentrate on the verbs which tell what you *did*. They make the incident easy to recall.

*I **found myself** yesterday near a huge box factory, located on a high hill. Running all around this building was a picket fence about this high.*

*I **walked up** to the factory, **threw open** the door, **walked in** and **found myself** in a long hallway.*

*At the far end of the hallway was a spiral staircase. I **walked up** this spiral staircase, **pushed open** a sliding door and **found myself** in a big room piled high with boxes. There were big boxes, middle-sized boxes and very small boxes.*

*Suddenly, the boxes came tumbling down around my head! I **woke with a start** — yawned, **stretched**, and **went back to sleep**.*

Thinking on Your Feet

Tonight, you will discover for yourself how easy it is to think on your feet—and you will have a good time doing it! No specific preparation for a talk is required. You and your classmates will participate in an exercise that will prove practical and enjoyable.

Please Do Some Friend—and Us—a Service

About this stage in the Course a person may often begin to realize that a minor miracle is being performed on some of his classmates—perhaps on him. He sees others making amazing progress — progress that a short time ago seemed quite impossible. Many persons, as a result of what they gain in this Course, look better, feel better, sleep better, work harder, have more fun out of life. Naturally they are enthusiastic — and grateful. In their enthusiasm, they tell their friends about the Course. (Often their friends have noticed a change and have asked what caused it.)

Perhaps some of these people who have heard about the Course from you would like information about it. Tonight you will be given cards on which you can write the names and addresses of your friends to whom you have spoken about the Course and who might like to take this Course. Your friends will be invited to a demonstration meeting or an open session where they may decide if this Course is what they want and need.

39

B—COMING OUT OF YOUR SHELL

Assignments and Awards

Reading: *The Quick and Easy Way to Effective Speaking,* Chapter 5 — "Vitalizing the Talk."

How to Win Friends and Influence People, review Part II — "Six Ways to Make People Like You."

The booklet, *A Quick and Easy Way to Learn to Speak in Public.*

Speaking: Sixty seconds — Talk on an incident that made you excited. Relive that experience with all the fervor you felt when it happened.

Awards: **Best Speech, Most Improvement and Special Award pencils.**

Here is one of the most entertaining and talked-about sessions in the entire Course. Many class members say this session has done more for them in building courage, confidence and animation than all the other four previous sessions combined. I doubt if there ever has been a more frightened speaker than Louise Lesley, who joined one of our classes in Lafayette, Indiana. Her experience in this session gave her a thrilling sense of freedom while speaking to others. She developed the ability to "pack a wallop" when she spoke — and she learned to speak with the courage and vigor she had long wanted. What Louise Lesley has done, countless others have done — and you can too!

We shall open the session by repeating twenty-nine words known to every man and woman who has taken the Course in the last thirty-five years.

We call it "I Know Men in the Ranks."

Since you will be called on to say these words, please memorize them. They are:

I know men in the ranks who are going to stay in the ranks. Why? I'll tell you why — simply because they haven't the ability to get things done.

After the class has been drilled to say "I Know Men in the Ranks" with meaning, emphasis and conviction (just as you would say it in a forceful speech), we will move on to the famous "Coming Out of Your Shell" part of the session.

Now You "Come Out of Your Shell"

I didn't invent this session. It grew — as all education ought to grow — out of the needs of the class members.

In this session you will have fun — and you will learn. It will do more than any other one session in the Course to rid you of self-consciousness and fear. This session gets results. It will "blast" you out of your shell. It will give you a new sense of freedom, ease and command. Frankly, I consider it one of the most helpful sessions of the Course.

If your instructor requests it, please come to this session with two newspapers.

Select the Right Topic

If you wish to get the greatest benefit out of this session, *be prepared!* Be sure you select an *incident* which made you excited or peeved and on which you can talk for *sixty seconds*. Relive this experience. Please include all the details and action necessary to make this experience vivid — but not so many that you get lost in boring explanation. Talk about any incident in which you got excited or angry. Surely you can recall one from your business, your profession, your community, your family or among your friends that irritates you. Get your temperature up to 212 degrees Fahrenheit and let 'er go. If you don't remember an experience of your own, please refer to the list of topics on Pages 111 to 117 of this book.

Read again the booklet *A Quick and Easy Way to Learn to Speak in Public*. This may help you choose a subject on which you could talk for twenty minutes — a subject on which you will have reserve power.

WARNING — Please be certain that in preparing this talk, you gather enough material to last *for one minute*. You may use an incident you gave at a previous session, provided it is boiling inside you. It is very important that you begin your talk with a *specific* example. Please start by telling us *what, when, where* and *how* you became peeved or excited, particularly what you did and how you did it. Act out your experience as much as possible to help us relive it with you.

Redouble Your Efforts to Prepare for the Sixth Session

To make a superb talk at the sixth session:

1. If you haven't yet done so, get busy applying the *one* rule you decided to apply back in Session 4.

2. Consciously, conscientiously, consistently, sincerely put that rule into practice — every time you get a chance. Herbert Spencer, the distinguished English philosopher, said, "The great aim of education is not knowledge but action." So act at once!

3. Tell the class what happened. Have no doubt: something *will have happened* — something worth talking about.

Talk About Yourself

Don't hesitate to talk about your own experiences so long as you relate them with modesty. Audiences are interested in what life has taught you. Your experiences *are* interesting when you use them to teach and not to boast.

Name of Instructor Tonight_____

Comments by Instructor:

Notes for My Talks at the Next Session:

Part A: A Talk on an Incident About Which I Can Speak Forcefully

Part B: A Talk on How I Used a Human Relations Rule

Session 6

A—How to Speak Convincingly
B—How to Win Friends

A—HOW TO SPEAK CONVINCINGLY

Assignments

Reading: *How to Stop Worrying and Start Living,* Part IV — "Seven Ways to Cultivate a Mental Attitude That Will Bring You Peace and Happiness," Chapters 12, 13 and 14.

Speaking: Twenty seconds — Talk on any incident about which you can speak forcefully.

Tonight you will take part in a novel and interesting event — you will find it one of the most thrilling, amusing and helpful experiences of the entire Course. Its purpose is to help you to forget yourself and to think only of your audience and your message. It will help you to develop force and spontaneity in your speaking, and it will help you to be more convincing in presenting your ideas.

Speak for twenty seconds on any incident you like. Don't bother to get a new talk — use one of your old ones. This is not a drill in speech construction, but an effort to get you to use animated and forceful delivery.

You Will Also Make a "Pick-It-Up-From-Here" Talk

You will get practice in thinking out a talk on your feet. You will take part in a "Pick-It-Up-From-Here" talk. You will enjoy building this chain talk with your fellow class members.

Have You Given Us the Names of Friends Who Might Profit by Taking the Course?

If, last week, you did not give your graduate assistants a list of names and addresses of your friends who might be interested in taking the Course, we will appreciate it if you will do so tonight.

We're Grateful for Your Help

We are grateful to those members of the class who have told their friends about this training and who handed the names of those friends to a graduate assistant last week. We will invite your friends to our next open meeting. (Wouldn't you enjoy going to the meeting with them? Why not plan to do it?)

B—HOW TO WIN FRIENDS

Assignments and Awards

Reading: *The Quick and Easy Way to Effective Speaking*, Chapter 6 — "Sharing the Talk With the Audience."

How to Win Friends and Influence People, review Part I — "Fundamental Techniques in Handling People" and Part II — "Six Ways to Make People Like You."

Speaking: Two minutes — Tell us one incident when you used one of the three "Fundamental Techniques in Handling People" or one of the "Six Ways to Make People Like You."

Awards: **Three copies of my book, *Lincoln the Unknown*.**

At Session 4 you were asked to select one of the "Fundamental Techniques in Handling People" or one of the "Six Ways to Make People Like You" and to apply that rule with sincerity.

Your Talk for Tonight

If you applied one of these rules sincerely and conscientiously, your talk will flow out of you tonight like water rushing down the side of a mountain.

Remember, the easiest things to talk about are your own experiences. So tell us about *one* of your experiences in using one of these human relations rules:

Fundamental Techniques in Handling People*

1. Don't criticize, condemn or complain.

2. Give honest, sincere appreciation.

3. Arouse in the other person an eager want.

Six Ways to Make People Like You*

4. Become genuinely interested in other people.

5. Smile.

6. Remember that a man's name is to him the sweetest and most important sound in any language.

7. Be a good listener. Encourage others to talk about themselves.

8. Talk in terms of the other man's interests.

9. Make the other person feel important — and do it *sincerely*.

*Numbered consecutively and underlined to help you hang them on your memory pegs.

Resolve to Abide by These Rules for the Rest of Your Life

I urge you with all the emphasis at my command to use these rules sincerely for the rest of your life. If you do — seven things will surely happen:

1. You will win friends rapidly.

2. You will be more influential.

3. You will likely forge ahead more rapidly in your business or profession.

4. You will — in the long run — increase your income.

5. You will be a much happier person.

6. You will improve your health.

7. Your children will be inspired by your example to lead richer, happier and more successful lives.

Three Books Awarded Tonight

Please vote for the three members you feel made the best talks on how they applied the rules for winning friends. Everyone who speaks on a current application of the rules, whether he has previously won a pencil or not, is eligible tonight. The three winners will each receive a copy of my book, *Lincoln the Unknown*.

Are You Acting More Enthusiastically?

Please remember that at Session 8 you are to tell us what happened when you used *five* times your usual amount of enthusiasm.

If you have been conscientious in your use of increased enthusiasm you will make a thrilling talk at Session 8. More important, however, you will be excited with the results that increased enthusiasm will have on your effectiveness.

How can you generate more enthusiasm? You must *act* more enthusiastically — then you will begin to *feel* more enthusiastic. You may go through a period of feeling unnatural. At first, your friends and even family may even make critical remarks about your strange and new personality. Be prepared for the questions such as "What has been feeding you raw meat?" (Your wife may even want to smell your breath!) Unnatural as you may seem and feel, remember your goal is to become a more lively and enthusiastic person.

You can be assured that this new animation and excitement will eventually become a part of your personality and will become natural for you. Then your effectiveness will be improved a hundred-fold. Start today!

Name of Instructor Tonight_____

Comments by Instructor:

Notes for My Talks at the Next Session:

Part A: A Talk on a Subject I Enjoy Talking About

Part B: A Magic Formula Talk

The Instructor's Magic Formula Talk	My Magic Formula Talk
His Example:	My Example: (Approximately 1 minute, 40 seconds)
His Point:	My Point: (Approximately 10 seconds)
His Reason:	My Reason: (Approximately 10 seconds)

Session 7

A—Thinking Out Your Talk
B—A Magic Formula to Get Action

A—THINKING OUT YOUR TALK

Assignments

Reading: *How to Stop Worrying and Start Living*, Part IV — "Seven Ways to Cultivate a Mental Attitude That Will Bring You Peace and Happiness," Chapters 15, 16, 17 and 18.

How to Win Friends and Influence People, Part IV — "Nine Ways to Change People Without Giving Offense or Arousing Resentment," Chapters 1, 2, 3, 4 and 5.

Speaking: Seventy-five seconds — Talk on some subject you will enjoy talking about and on which you have *earned* the right to talk. Your class members will judge your talk by the questions listed on Page 53.

This session will be opened with an exciting warm-up that will help you consolidate the gains you made in Session 5.

Now For Your Prepared Talk

You will talk for seventy-five seconds on any incident about which you have *earned the right to talk* and about which you are *eager to talk.* If you have children in school, what do you think they should be taught? Do you feel they are being taught subjects of no value to them? Tell us what changes you would make if you had the authority to change the curricula of our grade and high schools. *Prove what you say with an incident.*

Perhaps you can think of a better subject for yourself. Use it, or select a topic from the list on Pages 111 to 117.

Select the topic you like best and start preparing your talk as follows:

1. *Think* about it in your spare time.
2. *Make notes* of all ideas that occur to you.
3. *Talk the subject over* with your friends.
4. *Think it out*, but don't *write out* your talk and don't *memorize* it.

The most important rule above is "Think it out." If you think out your talk, you will find that one thought leads to another. Ideas will accumulate through reflective thinking. Illustrations and examples will flash into your mind. You will have enough material in a few days to last far beyond your seventy-five seconds of speaking time.

How to Listen Better

Tonight you will evaluate the talks of your fellow class members. As a result you will find it easier to develop better talks yourself. You will discover many ways in which you can improve as a speaker by improving the way you listen to others.

Ask yourself these questions as you listen:

As to the speaker

1. Does he know thoroughly what he is talking about — has he earned the right to talk on that subject?
2. Is he genuinely interested in what he is saying?
3. Is he eager to get his message over to his audience?
4. Is he having a good time giving his talk?

As to the talk

5. Is his example clear?

53

B—A MAGIC FORMULA TO GET ACTION

Assignments and Awards

Reading: *The Quick and Easy Way to Effective Speaking,* Chapter 7 — "Making the Short Talk to Get Action."

Speaking: Two minutes — A talk based on an experience which taught you a lesson. One which asks your audience to do something.

Awards: **Best Speech, Most Improvement and Special Award pencils.**

Every talk should fulfill one of the four speech purposes, namely: *to get action, to convince, to inform* or *to entertain.*

Tonight you will be taught a formula to use in preparing talks *to get action.* I call it the *Magic Formula,* because so many graduates testify that it has helped them get magical results from the speaking platform, in conferences, in sales talks, sales letters, interviews, advertisements — even at home with members of their families.

Please be reminded, however, that this formula is most practical for talks in which you are asking the audience *to take some action.* In other types of talks it is often desirable to use a different formula or a variation of this one.

The Magic Formula consists of three steps:

1. **Example**
2. **Point**
3. **Reason**

The Magic Formula at Work

Let me illustrate the Magic Formula at work. This talk was related by a class member.

EXAMPLE

(Here is the first step in this Magic Formula talk — his EXAMPLE. . . . an incident out of his life.)

"About a month and a half ago I was driving my daughter and her schoolmate back to their school in Bloomington after a weekend at our home. The traffic was heavier than usual, and the highway was slick after a rain. Before we started I remember asking the girls to fasten their seat belts. Linda, my daughter's friend, got a big kick out of using one for the first time.

"Suddenly something happened ahead on the parkway. I could see a car veer crazily toward the shoulder and a couple of people flying out. The cars in front of me stopped with a shriek of brakes and tires. I tried to turn into the shoulder, but I hit the car in front as it swerved to avoid the car in front of it. There was a loud noise as the cars came together and we were thrown from side to side. But the belts held. We were merely badly jostled. The driver in the car ahead of us was hurt badly when he was thrown against the dash and windshield. I couldn't help but think that all three of us would have been seriously hurt if we hadn't had our belts fastened. The state trooper who investigated the accident said we were lucky — the cars were so severely damaged, he thought someone in our car must have been hurt. When he found out seat belts had been fastened he said, 'Not lucky, just smart.'"

POINT

(Here is the second step of his Magic Formula talk — his POINT and by point is meant the action he asked his audience to take.)

"My point is: Require everyone to fasten seat belts every time you drive your car."

REASON

(Here is the third step of his Magic Formula talk — his REASON: The benefit his listeners will receive by doing what he asked in the point.)

"Because if you do you may prevent serious personal injury."

(Please note that his Magic Formula talk contained a specific incident out of his life; he asked for action in his point; and, in his reason, he gave a benefit for the listeners resulting from this action.)

Let's Examine the Steps of the Magic Formula

Your example:	*Should be an incident or an example out of your own life—one which taught you a lesson.*
Your point:	Answers the question: *What do you want us to do (that you think will help us)?*
Your reason:	Answers the question: *Why should we do it? (How will we benefit if we do what you ask?)*

Always Start Your Talk With the Example

In thinking out your talk, you may start with any of the three steps. In delivering your talk, however, *always begin with the example*. Why? Because the example captures the immediate attention of your audience and makes your talk sound conversational.

Please Prepare a Magic Formula Talk for Tonight

Please prepare a two-minute Magic Formula talk. Be sure that both your point and reason are brief, clear and specific — that your example is based on an experience that taught you a lesson. And remember, **your point must ask us to do something, the more specific, the better.**

How to Deliver Your Talk Tonight

If we would persuade others, we must be alert and alive ourselves. We must speak with sincerity and excitement. We must speak so that our listeners will feel that we believe every word we say. Woe to the salesman who does not believe in his own product!

Begin Now to Live More Enthusiastically

In Session 8, you will talk about your experiences in using increased enthusiasm. Let me suggest, therefore, that during the next week, you become *five* times as excited about your work, your family, your friends and your important activities as you usually are. By so doing, you are bound to have some experiences with increased enthusiasm — experiences that you will be eager to share with your listeners. If you get out of this training nothing more than greater enthusiasm, you may easily double your income and your happiness.

You will want to have a *current* incident of your use of *increased* enthusiasm. Do not rely on an age-old experience of a friend or relative. Begin today to use *increased* enthusiasm so that your talk will contain your own thrilling and inspiring story.

Name of Instructor Tonight_____

Comments by Instructor:

Notes for My Talks at the Next Session:

Part A: A Talk to Inform

Part B: A Talk on How I Used Increased Enthusiasm

Session 8

A—HOW TO MAKE YOUR IDEAS CLEAR

Assignments

Reading: *The Quick and Easy Way to Effective Speaking*, Chapter 8 — "Making the Talk to Inform."

How to Stop Worrying and Start Living, Part V — "The Perfect Way to Conquer Worry," and Part VI — "How to Keep From Worrying About Criticism."

Speaking: Ninety seconds — A talk to inform.

In the last session, you learned to make a talk to stimulate your audience to action, to do something. Perhaps, though, you have observed there are many speaking occasions when you do not wish action from your listeners; instead, you wish them to understand a process or a procedure. Our purpose this evening is to explain something to our listeners — to make a talk *to inform*.

Actually, we all make talks to inform far more often than we realize. We may direct a stranger to his destination, or we may attempt to explain to a mechanic exactly what is wrong with our automobile. Our purpose in all such talks is to get across our ideas as simply and as clearly as possible.

Tonight, you have ninety seconds in which to make a talk informing us of something. Here are some possible subjects:

> How to lay a tile floor.
> How to prepare a budget.
> The right way to reduce.

How to enjoy a vacation.
The enjoyment of popular music.
How to sail a boat.
The enjoyment of classical music.
How to build your own home.
How to give yourself a permanent wave.
The procedure of granting a bank loan.

You may choose any other subject, as long as you inform us of something. Try to fit the information within the framework of an incident.

Here are a few rules to guide you:

1. Use Simple Language

If it is necessary to use technical terms, please define them for the audience. If your idea is complicated or unknown to the audience, repeating the idea in different words may help your listeners to understand you.

2. Organize Your Material Carefully

In our previous talk — our main purpose was to get people to *do* something. In the talk to inform, however, our objective is to convey information to obtain understanding. One of the best ways of doing this is to organize your material logically, that is, have each idea lead naturally into the next idea. For example, if your talk were on the subject of driving an automobile, you would not skip from the automatic gear shift, to the seat adjustment, to the radio. Instead, you would probably begin your talk by discussing the preliminary steps to driving, such as starting the engine, releasing the brake, engaging the gears and checking traffic conditions.

3. Use Examples and Illustrations

The more familiar your example and illustrations are to your audience, the better they will understand you. For example, if you were attempting to explain jet propulsion to an audience unfamiliar with the subject, you might release an inflated toy balloon to show by comparison how the escaping air sends the balloon zooming much like a jet-propelled airplane.

4. Narrow Your Subject to the Important Points

If you have made the necessary preparations or if you have an adequate background for your talk to inform, you probably know more about the subject than the audience. There is a danger in this, in that you may become so wrapped up in your subject that you want to tell all you know about it. Actually, however, your audience cannot absorb at one sitting too many technical details or statistics. Please select and dwell on that aspect of the subject you can adequately cover in ninety seconds.

5. Summarize

To help you drive home the points or steps you have covered, take a few seconds at the end of your talk to summarize what you have said.

B—HOW TO MAKE THE MAGIC OF ENTHUSIASM WORK FOR YOU

Assignments and Awards

Reading: *How to Win Friends and Influence People*, Part III — "Twelve Ways to Win People to Your Way of Thinking," Chapters 1, 2, 3, 4, 5 and 6.

The booklet, *The Little Recognized Secret of Success*.

Speaking: Two minutes — Talk on how you used increased enthusiasm and what happened when you did.

Awards: **Best Speech pencil for the class member who, through his talk tonight, best convinced you that he has discovered the magic of enthusiasm. Most Improvement pencil for the class member who has made the most improvement in using enthusiasm in his talks. The Special Award pencil will be awarded as usual for some outstanding achievement.**

William James, the father of modern psychology, said, "What we do, compared with what we can do, is like comparing the waves on the top of the ocean with the ocean's mighty depths."

Are You Sufficiently Enthusiastic?

Many class members look shocked and unbelieving when an instructor tells them they should begin acting five times as alive and energetic as usual in all their daily activities. They seem to feel that such enthusiasm would be ridiculous. Believe me, it won't be. In many cases it might be the difference between failure and success.

The Man With Enthusiasm Wins

I have discussed enthusiasm as a factor of success with many men. For example, I interviewed Frederick Williamson, at one time president of the New York Central Railroad. I asked him what he felt was the secret of success in business. His reply was so significant in terms of what this session is all about, that I recorded it in its entirety in the booklet, *The Little Recognized Secret of Success*, which you received in Session 4. You were advised to read the booklet thoroughly and to start living more enthusiastically every day.

If you have not been increasing your enthusiasm during the past four weeks, I urge you to start right now to be more enthusiastic and animated. Remember: Look . . . act . . . feel . . . enthusiastic and you will be ENTHUSIASTIC.

If you began, four weeks ago to use *five* times as much enthusiasm as usual in your daily life, believe me, you will have a story to tell us tonight. Tell us how and when and where you used five times your usual amount of enthusiasm — and tell us of the results it brought you. Be sure your talk contains an incident.

Please, oh *please* don't confuse enthusiasm with noise. Webster says that *enthusiasm* is "Ardent zeal, or interest; fervor." *Fervor* is "intensity of expression." Webster doesn't say a word, in that connection, about noise or yelling or stamping. Real enthusiasm always comes from the inside out. It is an internal condition — a joyous excitement.

Talk Enthusiastically About Enthusiasm

As you make your two-minute talk on how you applied *increased* enthusiasm, I hope that you will be as Quintilian says, "A good man skilled in speaking." Deliver your talk with enthusiasm and animation. The best way to speak with enthusiasm is to choose some topic about which you feel deeply and about which you have a desire to speak. For example, I could not speak about tennis with enthusiasm even though I live in Forest Hills, the tennis capital of America. I spent my youth in the horse-and-buggy days on a Missouri farm — and I had no time or opportunity to play tennis. But if I were talking on gardening, I couldn't keep from talking with spirit and earnestness. Why? Because I am excited about gardening.

Mrs. Carnegie is wildly excited about our young daughter. Her love and enthusiasm for little Donna is boundless. Patrick Henry, in his "Give me liberty or give me death" talk probably didn't have any more deep feeling than does Mrs. Carnegie for our daughter; yet she doesn't raise her voice or shout when she talks to or about Donna. The point I am trying to make is this: Enthusiasm cannot be defined as loudness or yelling or chest-pounding. Real enthusiasm comes from the heart out, not from the lungs out. It is joyousness, not shouting.

As an example of the type of talk that can be made in this session here is an experience recently reported:

> "About three weeks ago my pastor called at my home and asked me to head a committee of men to renovate our church on Thirteenth Street. It was an old structure and badly in need of repair both inside and outside. After he left I sat down at my desk and tried to figure out on paper how all the necessary work could be done on the limited budget the pastor had given me. It seemed an impossible task. Most of the money would have to be spent on materials — there would be little or nothing left for labor.

> "The next day I was thinking about this problem and also about our eighth session assignment. The instructor told us that we were to act five times as enthusiastic as we normally act. It occurred to me that here was a good chance to put enthusiasm to the test. I called a meeting of the men whose names our minister had recommended. Ordinarily I would have been pretty casual, even negative in my approach. But I tried to look at the problem as a challenge to the members of the church. I briefly sketched what we were expected to do and then I asked the men what their ideas were. I warmed up to every suggestion. I greeted every idea with optimism and positively radiated enthusiasm. Soon the men began to catch some of my spirit. They, too, warmed to the subject. When I called an end to the meeting several stood outside still talking animatedly and four or five others prom-

ised to do some looking around for materials at the best prices. We had another meeting that week. The pastor was present and he said he had never known such warmhearted cooperation in all the years he had been at the church.

"This is what happened. We found that we could get the materials for the repairs much cheaper by the contacts of the men in the church. We set up a campaign called "Mission Twelve." On twelve evenings thirty-five men volunteered to come to the church and repaired the plaster, replaced the pews, changed the electrical circuits, laid a new tile floor. The women made coffee and the church lights glowed till after midnight. Everybody worked with a will and the whole job was completed on schedule in twelve nights.

"Believe me, friends, this was possible only because of enthusiasm. That whole congregation was fired up with eagerness and desire. I urge you to do as Dale Carnegie advises — become enthusiastic — and you will be more likely to get others to cooperate with you."

If you get nothing whatever out of this Course except a keener appreciation of the value of genuine enthusiasm — it may easily prove to be one of the most important discoveries of your life.

Speaking for myself, I can say that whatever little measure of success I have had in life has been due far more to my enthusiasm than any superior intelligence on my part. I was born enthusiastic. All my adult life I have been interested in enthusiasm as a factor of success.

I interviewed William Lyon Phelps, one of the most popular and beloved professors in the history of Yale and the author of *The Excitement of Teaching*. His remarks about the impact of enthusiasm are so profound that I have made them a part of my booklet, *The Little Recognized Secret of Success.*

The most glowing tribute ever paid the value of enthusiasm was paid by Sir Edward Victor Appleton, the world-famous physicist and Nobel Prize winner, whose discoveries led to such inventions as radar and round-the-world broadcasting. Read what he says about the value of enthusiasm in *The Little Recognized Secret of Success.*

You Get the Booklet
How to Remember Names

Before you leave the classroom tonight, be sure to get from a graduate assistant your copy of the booklet *How to Remember Names.* Please read this booklet in preparation for Session 9B.

Name of Instructor Tonight_____

Comments by Instructor:

Notes for My Talks at the Next Session:

Part A: A Talk with Mental and Emotional Impact

Part B: A Talk on How I Remembered the Name of a New Person I Met

Session 9

A—How to Stir Your Listeners
B—Steps to a Better Memory

A—HOW TO STIR YOUR LISTENERS
Assignments and Awards

Reading: *The Quick and Easy Way to Effective Speaking,*
Chapter 9 — "Making the Talk to Convince."
How to Stop Worrying and Start Living, Part VII
— "Six Ways to Prevent Fatigue and Worry and
Keep Your Energy and Spirits High."

Speaking: Ninety seconds — A talk in which you produce a
mental and emotional effect on your audience.

Awards: **Best Speech, Most Improvement and Special
Award pencils.**

If you are able to gain and hold the complete and favorable
attention of your listeners, you are a successful speaker. You
may have innumerable faults, but if you interest your audience,
who will care?

Concentrate tonight on the one big essential: producing a
mental and emotional effect on your listeners. How can you do
this? By speaking on an experience out of your own life that
produced a mental and emotional effect on you when it happened.

For example, around the turn of the century, a magazine pub-
lisher got wrought up because people had so little loyalty, enthusiasm and initiative. He had been troubled about this for
twenty years. One day he poured out his feelings in a short
article that later appeared in one of his magazines. That article,
dashed off at white heat, created a sensation. Orders for copies

of this article came pouring in from all over America. A hundred copies! A thousand! Ten thousand! The New York Central Railroad gave a copy to every one of its employees. So did hundreds of other corporations. The Russian army gave a copy to every Russian soldier in the Russo-Japanese War of 1904-05. And so did the Japanese army. Before the author died, forty million copies of that article had been reprinted — a world's record. I am referring to *A Message to Garcia*, by Elbert Hubbard.

Speak on a Subject You Feel Deeply

Tonight, do what Elbert Hubbard did. Speak out of the depths of your heart and feelings and convictions.

Talk about something that made you overwhelmingly happy, profoundly sorrowful, filled you with fear, dread or apprehension, filled you with a bitter resentment, or produced a beautiful love, friendship or devotion. Such a topic should fairly *explode* from you. For more specific suggestions, search the list of topics on Pages 111 to 117. This talk will be limited to ninety seconds.

B—STEPS TO A BETTER MEMORY

Assignments

Reading: *How to Win Friends and Influence People*, Part III — "Twelve Ways to Win People to Your Way of Thinking," Chapters 7, 8, 9, 10, 11 and 12.

Memory: Memory Pegs 11 through 21 (see Page 71).

Speaking: Sixty seconds — Tell us how, by applying the BRAMMS formula, you were able to remember the name of one new person you met within the last week.

In preparing for tonight's session, please review the first ten "memory peg" words and learn the next eleven.

The Twenty-one "Memory Peg" Words

One	— **Run**	Eleven	—	**Eleven (football eleven)**
Two	— **Zoo**	Twelve	—	**Shelve**
Three	— **Tree**	Thirteen	—	**Hurting**
Four	— **Door**	Fourteen	—	**Courting**
Five	— **Hive**	Fifteen	—	**Lifting**
Six	— **Sick**	Sixteen	—	**Licking**
Seven	— **Heaven**	Seventeen	—	**Leavening**
Eight	— **Gate**	Eighteen	—	**Waiting**
Nine	— **Wine**	Nineteen	—	**Pining**
Ten	— **Den**	Twenty	—	**Plenty (horn of plenty)**
		Twenty-one	—	**Dueling Gun**

You Learn How to Remember Names

At Session 6 we learned that "a man's name is to him the sweetest and most important sound in any language." Have you ever been embarrassed by your failure to practice this principle successfully? Tonight, your instructor will help you solve this common problem.

71

Are You Prepared for Session 10?

Don't forget that you will talk at Session 10B on how you controlled worry. Be sure you practice one or more of the thirty rules in the book *How to Stop Worrying and Start Living;* then report on the results of your experience.

Here is the best way to get the most out of Session 10: stop right now and look deeply into your current activities and associations. Decide honestly whether or not you are worrying about anything. (This often requires some soul-searching, since we occasionally worry without being conscious of it.) If you find anything, large or small, which is a source of undue concern, turn immediately to the *Worry* rules on Pages 109 to 111 of this book. Select one rule which best fits your situation and promise yourself that you will consciously use this rule during the coming week. Not only will you better understand the value of these rules, but you will also have a thrilling story to tell the class next week.

Name of Instructor Tonight_____

Comments by Instructor:

Notes for My Talk at the Next Session:

Part B: A Talk on How I Controlled Worry

Session 10

A—How to "Say a Few Words"
B—How to Control Worry and Reduce Tension

A—HOW TO "SAY A FEW WORDS"

Assignments

Reading: *The Quick and Easy Way to Effective Speaking,*
Chapter 10 — "Making Impromptu Talks."

How to Win Friends and Influence People, Part
IV — "Nine Ways to Change People Without
Giving Offense or Arousing Resentment," Chapters 6, 7, 8 and 9.

Review the booklet, *A Quick and Easy Way to
Learn to Speak in Public.*

Speaking: No talk to prepare. You will speak impromptu
for ninety seconds.

The chief purpose of Part A tonight is to enable you to discover for yourself how easy it is to talk for ninety seconds without any formal preparation whatever — when you are speaking about something that you know, something that you are eager to talk about.

Here Are Some Practical Suggestions

At tonight's session you will be given a topic for your talk which should suggest to you some experience or incident which has happened to you. Begin your talk by relating this experience or incident. Please refrain from unnecessary explanation. Get right down to cases. You will have no difficulty doing this if you start your talk with this opening: "I remember one time . . ." Include details. Use names and locations. Tell when the event happened. Conclude your talk by telling the audience what this experience or incident taught you.

Although no specific preparation is required for Part A tonight I urge you again to read the booklet, *A Quick and Easy Way to Learn to Speak in Public*. It is the guidebook to effective speaking.

B—HOW TO CONTROL WORRY AND REDUCE TENSION

Assignments and Awards

Reading: *How To Stop Worrying and Start Living*, Part X — "How I Conquered Worry."

Review the booklet, *How to Make Our Listeners Like Us*.

Speaking: Two minutes — An incident relating to how to control worry. A current example if possible.

Awards: **Copies of Dorothy Carnegie's Book *Don't Grow Old—Grow Up!* for the three best talks on "How I Conquered Fear" or "How I Controlled Worry."**

In preparing for this session, do not overlook any of the thirty rules on Pages 109 to 111 of this book. Your experience with any of these rules may inspire many of your listeners to lead happier lives.

If, after carefully evaluating your life, you find that you have had no personal experiences with worry since starting the Course, then you may use a story which is suggested to you by any of the following questions:

1. If you never worry, which rule do you use most often to solve your problem? (Use a specific example.)

2. If you have worried, which rule did you use or might you have used to solve your problems? (Use a specific example.)

3. Do you have a friend or relative who never worries? Which rule does he use to solve his problems? (Give a specific example.)

4. Has any friend or relative ever been a victim of worry? Which of the rules did help or might have helped him to solve his problems? (Give a specific example.)

You will find it easy to make an interesting and inspiring talk based on one of the above suggestions.

Here is an experience related by one of our class members:

A Tangible Result of Overcoming Worry

"Last February, after considerable engineering study, I submitted a report recommending a process change in our pulp bleachery that would result in gross annual chemical savings of $58,000. This would pay off the investment in only 22 months.

"A few weeks ago, some time after the Course started I was handed a copy of a letter from one of our higher executives to one of my superiors, stating essentially, 'Ed is off his rocker! Our data shows savings closer to $38,000.'

"In previous periods of my life I would have been crushed by such a blow. I remember one occasion when I almost lost my job because I was so worked up by a similar critical remark made by my superior. I was at a loss for days, worrying and stewing over what I should do next. This time, however, I was well charged with Dale Carnegie success-in-living principles. I took an entirely different attitude.

"Rather than worry over each little facet of this rather complex problem, as in the past, I decided to apply what I had learned in Chapter 4 of *How to Stop Worrying and Start Living*. I got the facts. I made an intensive re-study of all the work I had previously done, plus this: I compartmentalized each portion of the problem, analyzing each portion, ignoring the rest until the immediate portion was completely scrutinized, then going on to another.

"As a result, in ten days I was able to prove that, of five discrepancies brought to light, only one was an outright error on my part. The others stemmed from a previous report by others, furnished to me to make my original study. Incorporating the new data, I also was able to demonstrate that the gross savings were actually $45,000. This was a happy medium between my first claim and the higher executive's findings.

"I acted on the facts and the pay-off was revised to 27 months (which is still mighty attractive). The request for construction funds was resubmitted on that basis.

"So friends, when business problems beset you, analyze the facts, come to a decision, and act on that decision (point). You will overcome worry (reason)."

Work on Speech Construction

Tonight I suggest that you use the Magic Formula again. In preparing this talk, start with your example, then decide on your point and reason. You may wish to review Session 7B — the Magic Formula — before organizing your material. This will give you another opportunity to concentrate on speech construction. You will have two minutes for this talk.

Three Books Awarded Tonight

The three class members who receive the most votes will each receive a copy of *Don't Grow Old — Grow Up!* Everyone is eligible tonight — even those who have already won prizes.

Name of Instructor Tonight_____

Comments by Instructor:

Notes for My Talk at the Next Session:

Part A: A Talk on How I Used One of the Nine Ways to Change People Without Giving Offense or Arousing Resentment

Session 11

A—How to Change People Without Giving Offense or Arousing Resentment

B—Crashing Through

A—HOW TO CHANGE PEOPLE WITHOUT GIVING OFFENSE OR AROUSING RESENTMENT

Assignments

Reading: *How to Win Friends and Influence People*, review Part IV —"Nine Ways to Change People Without Giving Offense or Arousing Resentment."

Speaking: Ninety seconds — Talk on your application of one of the rules for changing people without giving offense or arousing resentment.

Tonight tell us in ninety seconds how, through the application of one of the "Nine Ways to Change People Without Giving Offense or Arousing Resentment," you have further developed yourself as a leader. Be prepared to tell at least one specific incident of your use of this rule which occurred within the past week.

Here are the "nine ways:"
1. Begin with praise and honest appreciation.
2. Call attention to people's mistakes indirectly.
3. Talk about your own mistakes before criticizing the other person.
4. Ask questions instead of giving orders.
5. Let the other man save his face.

6. Praise the slightest improvement and praise every improvement. Be "hearty in your approbation and lavish in your praise."
7. Give the other person a fine reputation to live up to.
8. Use encouragement. Make the fault seem easy to correct.
9. Make the other person happy about doing the thing you suggest.

B—CRASHING THROUGH

Assignment and Award

Reading: *The Quick and Easy Way to Effective Speaking,* Chapter 11 —"Delivering the Talk."

Speaking: No talk to prepare.

Award: **A copy of *Dale Carnegie's Scrapbook* to the class member who receives the greatest number of votes for having "crashed through" the best.**

Expect some happy surprises tonight! The instructor will put you through several easy exercises — exercises that will give you a new freedom and a new ease in speaking — and that will, among other things, help you overcome that great enemy of effective speaking — self-consciousness.

Evaluate Your Own Personality

Tonight you will be given a booklet entitled *How to Rate Your Personal Abilities.* I suggest that you take this booklet home and carefully rate yourself. No one else need see the ratings — they are for your own personal use.

Are You Living Next Week's Assignment?

Please begin now to intensify your preparation for Session 12. Renew your efforts in applying one of the "Twelve Ways to Win People to Your Way of Thinking" from *How to Win Friends and Influence People*.

Which rule did you select? Perhaps the one you break most often. Keep on using it — you will find it easier all the time — you will marvel at the results it produces.

At Session 12B (How to Get Enthusiastic Cooperation), tell us how you applied the rule you have chosen and how it worked.

Please remember that, while this rule is the subject of a talk you will give at Session 12B, you are far more interested in improving your relationships with other people. Use your rule conscientiously, then you will realize the miraculous benefits of this whole training. You owe it to yourself to have a *current* example of the use of one of these rules to tell the class at Session 12B.

Tonight You Get a Guidebook for Effective Conference Work

In *How to Save Time and Get Better Results in Conferences,* I relate an experience of my friend, Leon Shimkin, Chairman of the Board of Directors of Simon & Schuster, Inc., one of America's leading publishers. I urge you to memorize the four problem-solving questions in the booklet. Also please study the booklet during the next two weeks until you have a good working knowledge of the rules for both conference leadership and conference participation. The effort you spend studying this booklet now will be repaid many times over.

Prepare to Vote for Future Graduate Assistants

At the thirteenth session you will do some voting that is of vital interest to future classes. You will vote for the four persons in your class who are best fitted to serve as graduate assistants. Please begin to think about this now. Consider first what qualifications a graduate assistant should have. Surely by now you know the qualities you like in a graduate assistant. Then consider which four members in the class are most bountifully supplied with these attributes.

The men and women thus honored by the class will be considered for future graduate assistants. Your present graduate assistants will also make their nominations. The final decision as to which members of your class will be selected as graduate assistants will be made by the person who is in charge of The Dale Carnegie Course in your city.

Name of Instructor Tonight_____

Comments by Instructor:

Notes for My Talks at the Next Session:

Part A: A Speech of Introduction

Part B: A Talk on How I Used a Rule to Get Enthusiastic Cooperation

Session 12

A—How to Introduce a Speaker
B—How to Get Enthusiastic Cooperation

A—HOW TO INTRODUCE A SPEAKER

Assignments

Reading: *The Quick and Easy Way to Effective Speaking,* Chapter 12—"Introducing Speakers, Presenting and Accepting Awards."

Speaking: Sixty seconds — A Speech of Introduction.

Perhaps you have observed that a well-organized and well-delivered introduction of a speaker not only is a credit to the introducer, but, what is more important, assists the speaker in getting off to a flying start. Your assignment tonight is to introduce to the "audience" a speaker (and his topic) who is not a class member, graduate assistant or instructor — someone who is still living — perhaps even a member of your own family.

How do you organize your ideas in making a Speech of Introduction? One way is to use the *T—I—S Formula*, as follows:

1. **T** stands for **Topic.** Speak first of the topic, giving the exact title of the talk if it is known to you.

2. **I** stands for **Importance.** Then tell the audience why this topic is important to *this* particular group.

3. **S** stands for **Speaker.** Now give the audience your speaker's qualifications. As the final two or three words of your introduction, give the speaker's name. Be sure to say it clearly and distinctly.

How do you deliver your talk? Here are four suggestions:

1. Be brief. It is not necessary to speak over sixty seconds — preferably less.
2. Speak informally — just as you would across the dinner table.
3. Be enthusiastic about your assignment. Be animated. Be alive. Make your introduction sparkle. You owe it to the person you are introducing and to your audience to put a lot of zip into your talk. Act as though it were a real privilege to introduce this speaker — feel happy about it — talk with real animation.
4. Above all, be warmly sincere. It is discourteous to be otherwise.

Suppose you are scheduled to introduce William Howard Jones, a certified public accountant, as a speaker at a business club luncheon. You might introduce him in this manner:

T (Topic)	We are to hear a talk on "Why Businesses Fail."
	Here is a letter from Dun and Bradstreet in which they make this startling statement:
I (Importance)	"Of all new concerns starting in business this year, about sixty-five per cent will fail to reach a sixth birthday." Since we are all business people, we are eager to hear how we can prevent this calamity from happening to us.
S (Speaker)	Our speaker is an accountant. He has had seven articles published in *The Accounting Review* and in *The Journal of Accounting Procedure,* and he has also done special studies for the National Association of Cost Accountants. Ladies and Gentlemen (pause), WILLIAM H. JONES! . . . Mr. Jones.

An effective introduction need not be long. You will have one minute for this talk.

WARNING:

1. In introducing a speaker, **NEVER** try to be humorous unless you are *positive* that the mantle of Mark Twain has descended on your shoulders.

2. **NEVER** memorize a speech of introduction.

Start Preparing for Next Week

During the next seven days, I strongly urge you to study the rules in the booklet, *How to Save Time and Get Better Results in Conferences*, and prepare yourself better to solve problems.

Every class member should read this booklet at least twice before Session 13.

B—HOW TO GET ENTHUSIASTIC COOPERATION

Assignments and Awards

Reading: *How to Win Friends and Influence People,* review Part III —"Twelve Ways to Win People to Your Way of Thinking."

Speaking: Two minutes — A talk based on your experience in using one of the rules for winning people to your way of thinking which occurred within the past three weeks.

Awards: **Three Human Relations Award pencils.**

When the elder John D. Rockefeller was setting up the Standard Oil Company, he said to his partner, Matthew Brush, "The ability to get along with people is as purchasable as sugar and coffee. I will pay more for that ability than any ability under the sun." Mr. Rockefeller was talking about *leadership* — the topic we deal with tonight. To gather material for your talk, please spend the week applying one of the rules listed below.

Twelve Ways to Win People to Your Way of Thinking*

10. The only way to get the best of an <u>argument</u> is to avoid it.

11. Show <u>respect</u> for the other man's opinion. Never tell a man he is wrong.

12. If you are wrong, <u>admit</u> it quickly and emphatically.

13. Begin in a <u>friendly</u> way.

14. Get the other person saying <u>"yes, yes"</u> immediately.

15. Let the other man do a great deal of the <u>talking</u>.

16. Let the other man feel that the <u>idea</u> is his.

17. Try honestly to see things from the other person's point of <u>view</u>.

18. Be <u>sympathetic</u> with the other person's ideas and desires.

19. Appeal to the <u>nobler</u> motives.

20. <u>Dramatize</u> your ideas.

21. Throw down a <u>challenge</u>.

*Numbered consecutively and underlined for pegging in addition to the rules in Session 6.

Use one of these rules at your office or home, or in your business and social contacts just as you did in preparation for Sessions 6B and 11A. Then come to class and tell us your experience. Please use the Magic Formula in organizing your talk. (You may wish to review Session 7B in this book.) Your talk will give evidence of your ability to practice these rules of leadership. It should be one of your best.

Three Pencils Awarded Tonight

Vote for the three class members who made the best talks on a current application of one of the "Twelve Ways to Win People to Your Way of Thinking." The winners will receive white pencils inscribed with the words, "Human Relations Award." Everyone who speaks on a current application of one of these rules, whether he has won an award previously or not, is eligible.

Will Any of Your Friends Be in the Next Dale Carnegie Class in Your Community?

You were kind enough, recently, to hand to a graduate assistant the names and addresses of some of your friends. You had talked with these people, and you felt that they might be interested in taking the Course.

Your friends, whose names you gave us, will be invited to the next open meeting or demonstration meeting held here. This will give them an opportunity to learn what the Course has done for other people. No doubt it will give them a good idea of what the Course might do to help them.

If, as a result of this thoughtful act, your friends take the Course, you know from your own experience how grateful they will be to you. We are grateful to you, too, for your cooperation.

In the past few weeks you have probably told other friends, associates or employees about this training: how you and all your classmates have gained confidence and enthusiasm — how much better you get along with people and enjoy life more — how you can now speak to groups of people and what an all-around good time you are having in class.

To permit you time to think about this, we will not ask for names and addresses of these additional friends until Session 13. (If you should think of someone right now, please note his name on the appropriate page at the back of this booklet.) Your friends will be invited to attend our next open meeting. Plan to come and bring them with you. You will enjoy it.

Name of Instructor Tonight_____

Comments by Instructor:

Notes for My Talk at the Next Session:

Part A: My Prepared Speech Contest Talk

Session 13

A—Prepared Speech Contest

B—How to Solve Problems and Get Better Results in Conferences

A—PREPARED SPEECH CONTEST

Assignments and Award

Reading: *The Quick and Easy Way to Effective Speaking,*
Chapter 13 — "Organizing the Longer Talk."
Review the booklet *A Quick and Easy Way to
Learn to Speak in Public.*

Speaking: Ninety seconds — A prepared talk for the championship contest, using one incident and other techniques of effective speaking you have learned in the Course.

Award: **Prepared Speech Champion pencil.**

Your class will hold a contest tonight to select its Prepared Speech Champion.

Select your own topic and come to class tonight fired with a determination to give a superb ninety-second talk. Do not allow your ambition to trap you into memorizing your talk. Present your message with a vivid, living example, as specified in *A Quick and Easy Way to Learn to Speak in Public.*

The voting will be by secret ballot. Please vote for the person you believe made the best prepared talk. The person who receives the highest number of votes will receive a bronze pencil inscribed "Prepared Speech Champion."

Class Will Vote for Graduate Assistants

Just before the first part of this session ends, the class will vote, by secret ballot, for four of its members as possible graduate assistants for future classes.

This is the most important vote you will cast in the entire Course. Please give it serious thought. Remember, women are eligible to become graduate assistants.

Your graduate assistants will not look at these votes after they collect them but will at once seal them in an envelope, together with their own recommendations, and mail them to the sponsor of the Course in your territory. The sponsor will be guided largely by your voting in selecting the candidates who are to be invited to attend the next training school for graduate assistants.

Don't vote for a man just because he is a "good fellow;" don't vote for a man merely because he has campaigned for the job. Remember, being a graduate assistant requires integrity and sincerity. Try to select men and women who will be efficient and who will be a credit to your class and to the Dale Carnegie ideals.

B—HOW TO SOLVE PROBLEMS AND GET BETTER RESULTS IN CONFERENCES

Assignments

Reading: Review the booklet, *How to Save Time and Get Better Results in Conferences.*

How to Stop Worrying and Start Living, Part IX — "How to Lessen Your Financial Worries."

How to Win Friends and Influence People, Part V — "Letters That Produced Miraculous Results."

Memory: The four problem-solving questions (see Page 96).

Speaking: Class members will make conference talks on problems assigned by the instructor during the session.

Many of you take this Course to win more outstanding positions of leadership in society, in politics, in your business or profession. To become a successful leader, you should be able to take an active part in conferences and discussions and to lead meetings.

Some class members say, "I'm not interested in conferences — I never take part in them."

Nonsense! Everybody who can *speak* takes part almost daily in conferences. When a husband and wife take up the question of what motion picture to see tonight, they are engaging in a family conference. When a mother talks with her children about whether or not they ought to play with tough little Johnny Blank down the street, they are participating in a conference. What is a committee meeting or a board of directors meeting but a conference — and what is the chairman but a conference leader!

95

What You Learn in This Session

Because we all engage in conferences almost daily, this session is intensely practical. In it you learn:

1. The four problem-solving questions and how to use them in solving a group or personal problem.

2. How to *talk* effectively in a conference.

3. How to *take part* in a conference.

4. How to *lead* a conference.

5. How to make a *report* on a conference.

Please Review the Booklet How to Save Time And Get Better Results in Conferences

Please reread and study the booklet *How to Save Time and Get Better Results in Conferences*. Make it your handbook for all conference work. Why? Because it will save you time and help you put across the ideas *you* have in *your* mind.

Please Memorize These Four Questions

The instructor's first job tonight is to make sure that all class members know the four questions to ask in any problem-solving conference. So please memorize them. They are:

1. What is the problem?

2. What are the causes of the problem?

3. What are the possible solutions?

4. What is the best possible solution?

A Demonstration of a Conference

You will take part in a demonstration conference led by your instructor on the subject "Some fifty thousand people are killed annually on our highways." (*Consumers' Research Bulletin,* U.S.A.) If possible, please obtain statistics or other facts concerning this problem in your community. Such information is available at your local police department or automobile club.

Throughout this demonstration of a conference, the instructor will observe the rules for *leading* a conference. The class members will observe the rules for *participating* in a conference.

You Learn How to Participate in a Conference

As a participant in a conference, your purpose in speaking is to convince or to influence people to your way of thinking. To convince your listeners, you should be both brief and clear — so, for your conference talks, let me suggest this simple formula:

1. **Point** (your suggested solution to the problem under discussion).
2. **Example** (your proof, evidence or testimony that your suggested solution will solve the problem under discussion).

So, when you offer a possible solution, please prepare it as follows:

1. Decide on your point or suggested solution to the problem. Boil it down to the fewest possible words.
2. Present some evidence which suggests that your solution might solve the problem. Your evidence should be in the form of an exhibit, demonstration, statistics, the testimony of an expert, an analogy or an incident type of example.

State first your suggested solution to the problem in one brief, clear sentence, and then give your evidence to show that your solution will work.

Small Group Conferences

Your instructor will reseat the class in small groups of about six each. The groups will hold problem-solving conferences until the end of the session.

Please Submit the Names of Persons
Who Might Be Interested in This Course

Tonight, your instructor will ask you to submit, on forms to be provided, the names of persons you believe would benefit from this Course. Thank you.

Name of Instructor Tonight_____

Comments by Instructor:

Notes for My Talk at the Next Session:

Part B: A Talk on the Chief Benefit I Received from the Course

Session 14

A—Impromptu Speech Contest
B—Evaluating Your Progress

A—IMPROMPTU SPEECH CONTEST

Assignments and Award

Reading: *How to Stop Worrying and Start Living*, Part VIII — "How to Find the Kind of Work in Which You May Be Happy and Successful."

Review *The Quick and Easy Way to Effective Speaking*, Chapter 10 — "Making Impromptu Talks."

Review the booklets, *A Quick and Easy Way to Learn to Speak in Public* and *How to Make Our Listeners Like Us.*

Speaking: Ninety-second impromptu talk. No preparation.

Award: **Impromptu Speech Champion pencil.**

Tonight you will prove beyond a reasonable doubt that you have conquered your fear of impromptu speaking. You will participate in a contest to select the Impromptu Speech Champion of your class.

A graduate assistant will supply your topic just before you speak. The challenge to you will be to begin immediately with an example and think through your talk on your feet while you are delivering it.

The voting will be by secret ballot. (The person who won the Prepared Speech Contest last week is ineligible; so please don't vote for him tonight.) Please vote for the person who made the best impromptu talk; and, of course, that will be the person who used the best example. The person who receives the highest number of votes will receive a bronze pencil inscribed "Impromptu Speech Champion."

B—EVALUATING YOUR PROGRESS

Assignments and Award

Reading: *The Quick and Easy Way to Effective Speaking,* Chapter 14 — "Applying What You Have Learned."

How to Win Friends and Influence People, Part VI — "Seven Rules for Making Your Home Life Happier."

Speaking: Two minutes — Relate a specific incident which best illustrates the major benefit you have received in the Course.

Award: **Highest Award for Achievement pencil.**

The award will be presented to the member, who in the opinion of the class, gives the most sincere and solid evidence of the benefit received from the Course.

In preparing your talk tonight, ask yourself:

"What single experience best illustrates the major benefit I have received since starting the Course? (Self-confidence, Poise, Courage, Freedom from worry, Ability to control fear, More joyous living, Better ability to understand and get along with

101

people, More effective personal and/or public speaking, etc.)"

Give special attention to the example you use in this talk tonight. Your classmates will vote for the person who convinces them by his example that he has made the most progress in your class.

How will they know which member has made the most progress in the Course? By listening attentively to all the talks, they will be influenced by the person who makes the most sincere talk and *who gives the best evidence* that he has benefited most from this training.

The winner will receive a bronze pencil inscribed "Highest Award for Achievement," so dig right in and prepare enthusiastically. In this way you'll be primed to deliver a convincing talk — probably your most effective of the whole Course. And, remember, your position in the final vote depends largely on the clarity of the evidence you submit, specific and relevant proof that you have made actual progress as a result of your experiences while taking the Course, facts that impress the class with the Course's impact on your life. **What is the best type of proof? A clear, specific incident!**

Everyone is Eligible

Even though you may already be the proud owner of an award won at a previous session, you are eligible for this final and important award.

Did You Turn in Your List of People Who May Be Interested in Taking This Course?

If, last week, you did not turn in a list of your friends or relatives who might profit by taking this Course, please do so tonight. You will be doing a favor both for them and for us.

Guests Are Welcome Tonight

You may bring guests to this session if there is space in your meeting room. It might be wise to check this in advance with your graduate assistants or your instructor.

SESSION 14

Name of Instructor Tonight_____

Comments by Instructor:

A FINAL WORD

You have developed in the past few months skills which will help you to get along better with other people; you have learned to speak with ease in business and social interviews and before groups; you have improved your memory; and you have developed confidence, poise and your leadership ability.

I urge that you continue to grow by the constant practice of the skills you have gained and the habits you have formed so that you may attain a happier, fuller and more successful life.

I hope that you will some day look back upon this training as one of the milestones of your career.

Good-bye. Good luck. And may God keep on loving you always.

Dale Carnegie

WHERE DO YOU GO FROM HERE?

If you want to continue to improve your human relations, to become a better salesman, a more effective administrator or executive and to form stimulating, pleasant friendships, here are four suggestions:

1. Take the Dale Carnegie Sales Course, if you sell or supervise selling (for men and women).

2. Take the Dorothy Carnegie Course in Personal Development for Women (for women only).

3. Take the Dale Carnegie Supervision and Management Seminar if you are in an administrative or executive position as a manager or supervisor.

4. Bank or retail personnel may wish to investigate the benefits to be obtained from the Dale Carnegie Customer Relations Course.

Information regarding these Courses may be secured from your local Carnegie Courses sponsor or by writing to:

DALE CARNEGIE & ASSOCIATES, INC.
1475 Franklin Avenue
Garden City, New York 11530

RULES FROM *HOW TO WIN FRIENDS AND INFLUENCE PEOPLE*

Fundamental Techniques in Handling People

1. Don't criticize, condemn or complain.

2. Give honest, sincere appreciation.

3. Arouse in the other person an eager want.

Six Ways to Make People Like You

1. Become genuinely <u>interested</u> in other people.
2. <u>Smile.</u>
3. Remember that a man's <u>name</u> is to him the sweetest and most important sound in any language.
4. Be a good <u>listener.</u> Encourage others to talk about themselves.
5. <u>Talk</u> in terms of the other man's interests.
6. Make the other person feel <u>important</u> — and do it *sincerely*.

Twelve Ways to Win People to Your Way of Thinking

1. The only way to get the best of an <u>argument</u> is to avoid it.
2. Show <u>respect</u> for the other man's opinion. Never tell a man he is wrong.
3. If you are wrong, <u>admit</u> it quickly and emphatically.
4. Begin in a <u>friendly</u> way.
5. Get the other person saying "yes, yes" immediately.
6. Let the other man do a great deal of the <u>talking.</u>
7. Let the other man feel that the <u>idea</u> is his.
8. Try honestly to see things from the other person's point of <u>view.</u>
9. Be <u>sympathetic</u> with the other person's ideas and desires.
10. Appeal to the <u>nobler</u> motives.
11. <u>Dramatize</u> your ideas.
12. Throw down a <u>challenge.</u>

Nine Ways to Change People Without Giving Offense or Arousing Resentment

1. Begin with praise and honest appreciation.
2. Call attention to people's mistakes indirectly.
3. Talk about your own mistakes before criticizing the other person.
4. Ask questions instead of giving direct orders.
5. Let the other man save his face.
6. Praise the slightest improvement and praise every improvement. Be "hearty in your approbation and lavish in your praise."
7. Give the other person a fine reputation to live up to.
8. Use encouragement. Make the fault seem easy to correct.
9. Make the other person happy about doing the thing you suggest.

Seven Rules for Making Your Home Life Happier

1. Don't nag.
2. Don't try to make your partner over.
3. Don't criticize.
4. Give honest appreciation.
5. Pay little attentions.
6. Be courteous.
7. Read a good book on the sexual side of marriage.

RULES FROM *HOW TO STOP WORRYING AND START LIVING*

PART ONE: Fundamental Rules for Overcoming Worry

Rule 1: Live in "day-tight compartments."
Rule 2: How to face trouble.
    a. Ask yourself, "What is the worst that can possibly happen?"
    b. Prepare to accept the worst.
    c. Try to improve on the worst.
Rule 3: Remind yourself of the exorbitant price you can pay for worry in terms of your health.

PART TWO: Basic Techniques in Analyzing Worry

Rule 1: Get all the facts.
Rule 2: Weigh all the facts — then come to a decision.
Rule 3: Once a decision is reached, act!
Rule 4: Write out and answer the following questions:
    a. What is the problem?
    b. What are the causes of the problem?
    c. What are the possible solutions?
    d. What is the best possible solution?

PART THREE: How to Break the Worry Habit Before It Breaks You

Rule 1: Keep busy.
Rule 2: Don't fuss about trifles.
Rule 3: Use the law of averages to outlaw your worries.
Rule 4: Cooperate with the inevitable.
Rule 5: Decide just how much anxiety a thing may be worth and refuse to give it more.
Rule 6: Don't worry about the past.

PART FOUR: Seven Ways to Cultivate a Mental Attitude That Will Bring You Peace and Happiness

Rule 1: Fill your mind with thoughts of peace, courage, health and hope.

Rule 2: Never try to get even with your enemies.

Rule 3: Expect ingratitude.

Rule 4: Count your blessings — not your troubles.

Rule 5: Do not imitate others.

Rule 6: Try to profit from your losses.

Rule 7: Create happiness for others.

PART FIVE: The Perfect Way to Conquer Worry

Rule: Pray.

PART SIX: How to Keep From Worrying About Criticism

Rule 1: Remember that unjust criticism is often a disguised compliment.

Rule 2: Do the very best you can.

Rule 3: Analyze your own mistakes and criticize yourself.

PART SEVEN: Six Ways to Prevent Fatigue and Worry and Keep Your Energy and Spirits High

Rule 1: Rest before you get tired.

Rule 2: Learn to relax at your work.

Rule 3: If you are a housewife, protect your health and appearance by relaxing at home.

Rule 4: Apply these four good working habits:

    a. Clear your desk of all papers except those relating to the immediate problem at hand.

    b. Do things in the order of their importance.

    c. When you face a problem, solve it then and there if you have the facts necessary to make a decision.

    d. Learn to organize, deputize and supervise.

Rule 5: Put enthusiasm into your work.

Rule 6: Don't worry about insomnia.

TOPICS FOR TALKS

I know from experience that some class members have difficulty in selecting a topic on which to speak. Because the topic on which you speak has so much to do with your progress in developing courage and self-confidence, I have prepared the list of topics which follows. Whenever you need a topic for a talk, please consult this list — then select a topic which brings back vivid and exciting impressions of the incident as it happened. That topic should be one:

    a. You have earned the right to talk about.

    b. You feel deeply.

    c. You are eager to relate.

Here are the topics:

Business

1. The biggest sale I ever made — and the thrill I got from it.
2. How I earned my first dollar.
3. How and why I got into my present line of work.
4. How and why I failed in business.
5. How one idea increased my income.
6. What I like or dislike about my boss.
7. I like my present job because . . .
8. The kind of job I'd like to have.
9. The worst headache I ever had in business.

10. The best (or worst) investment I ever made in my life.
11. The best sale I ever made.
12. How I got my first job — and why I am glad I lost it.
13. My boss was good to me.
14. My experience of approaching my first customer — and the results.

Childhood

15. My favorite teacher — and why I liked her (or him).
16. The excitement of receiving my high school diploma.
17. A lesson I learned at school.
18. My neighbor's youngsters "burn me up" because . . .
19. The thrill of getting my first bicycle.
20. My first day at school.
21. What I think of the education I got in grade school — or high school — or college — and why.

Family

22. How I felt when my home burned down.
23. A mistake I made in rearing my children.
24. A crisis that my wife (or husband) and I faced.
25. The thrill I got in watching my son (or daughter) being graduated from high school or college.
26. My most pleasant memory of my mother (or father).
27. A mistake I made in building my home.
28. A lesson my children have taught me.
29. How a baby changed our home.
30. What I want most to give my children.
31. I was homesick.
32. How deeply I wish I had been better to my mother and father.
33. I became a father.
34. My wedding.
35. I lost a loved one.
36. How my son (or daughter) embarrassed me.
37. The most humorous thing my child ever said or did.
38. I was proud of my son (or daughter) because . . .

39. I was proud of my husband (or wife) because . . .
40. I was proud of my father (or mother) because . . .
41. Why my marriage failed.
42. An incident that taught me that my father (or mother) was courageous.

People

43. My hero — and why I worship him (or her).
44. The most friendly deed that was ever done for me.
45. The most friendly deed that I did for someone else.
46. The happiest couple I know — and why they are happy.
47. The most discourteous service I had to endure.
48. The most unforgettable character I ever met.
49. The pleasure I get from praising a friend (relative or employee).
50. The finest woman (or man) I have ever known — and what I like about her (or him).
51. My most moving human relations experience.
52. I made an enemy.
53. My favorite character — and how he has inspired me.
54. The person who has influenced me most.
55. The most courageous act I ever witnessed.
56. Friendliness made my journey pleasanter.
57. It's a small world.
58. My favorite speaker — and why I like him.
59. My home town — and what I like about it.
60. A stranger befriended me.
61. What I learned by becoming interested in a stranger.
62. I offended someone because . . .

Personal

63. The best advice I ever received — and how it helped me.
64. The most exciting thing I ever did.
65. My first encounter with the law.
66. The most embarrassing thing I ever did.
67. The best friend I ever had.
68. My most important decision and how I made it.

69. I was scared.
70. The meanest prank I ever played.
71. My most enjoyable Christmas.
72. An enchanted evening I will always remember.
73. The greatest help I ever received.
74. The longest minute I ever spent.
75. I was misled by an advertisement.
76. An unforgettable experience with "puppy love."
77. How I cured a cold.
78. My anxiety over the illness of a loved one.
79. I was patient and it paid off.
80. My closest call with death.
81. My worst automobile accident — and what caused it.
82. The strangest coincidence I ever heard of (or witnessed).
83. This happened to me — and I can't explain it.
84. Why I believe in the old maxim "A stitch in time saves nine."
85. My big moment.
86. The greatest compliment I ever received.
87. I made it myself.
88. How one idea increased my happiness.
89. I am my own worst enemy because . . .
90. My first ocean crossing.
91. I made a friend.
92. I was crushed by criticism.
93. My favorite song — and the memories it brings to me.
94. My favorite opera — and why I like it.
95. My favorite food — and why I like it.
96. My favorite painting — and why I like it.
97. My favorite motto — and what it has meant to me.
98. The greatest tragedy of my life.
99. The most stupid thing I ever did.
100. The strongest conviction of my life.
101. My most moving experience.
102. I was jilted.
103. The most important lesson I have learned.
104. My biggest battle with myself.

105. My greatest handicap.
106. My secret ambition.
107. My greatest musical experience.
108. The biggest surprise of my life.
109. I nearly drowned.
110. How I conquered my biggest fear (or worry) problem.
111. My most unforgettable experience in the army, navy, marines or air force.
112. How worry robbed me of health and happiness.
113. How timidity and shyness have stood in my way.
114. Why I quit drinking.
115. Why I quit gambling.
116. When a fellow needs a friend.
117. I was cheated.
118. Let me cry on your shoulder.
119. Man, I was frightened!
120. I learned my lesson the hard way.
121. I'll never do that again.
122. My initiation into . . .
123. I had forgotten my wallet.
124. I felt like "two cents."
125. My favorite pet — and why I like him (or her).
126. My favorite toy — and why I liked it.
127. If I had my life to live over, I would . . . because . . .
128. I have seen a ghost.
129. I never felt more lonely in my life.
130. The most disappointing day of my life.
131. A bit of showmanship I shall never forget.
132. When I prayed the hardest — and why.
133. My experiences as a hitchhiker.
134. How I ruined my health.
135. I was "mad as a wet hen."
136. The most exciting news I ever received by telephone, telegraph or letter — and how it affected me.
137. Why I quit smoking.
138. I was seasick (or airsick).
139. I wish I had never said that.

140. I did it on the spur of the moment.
141. I was drafted.
142. My first . . . and how it thrilled me.
143. I was inspired by . . .
144. I visited a friend on the farm.
145. I got into trouble because I broke a window (or anything else that you might have broken).
146. I have lived in bitter poverty — and what it did for me.
147. I won a medal because . . . and the thrill it gave me.
148. How I felt when the doctor told me to slow down.
149. Love at first sight.
150. My greatest disappointment.
151. My dog saved my life.
152. The saddest moment in my life.
153. I turned to prayer as a last resort.
154. I was robbed (or held up).
155. My greatest scare in the dark.
156. The happiest recollection of my childhood.
157. I wish I could relive this one experience.

Recreation

158. How I keep fit.
159. The most exciting sports event I ever watched.
160. The old swimming hole.
161. The thrill I had scoring a touchdown.
162. The best book I ever read — the best play or the best film I ever saw — and why I liked it best.
163. The most wonderful vacation I ever had.
164. My most successful hunting trip.
165. My most successful fishing trip.
166. My experience at the circus.
167. My experience at the county fair.
168. The thrill of owning my first automobile.
169. How I became interested in my hobby.
170. The most fun I ever had.

Social

171. My first date.
172. The most exciting date I ever had.
173. A birthday party I will always remember.
174. A dinner I will always remember.
175. Why I am happy that I joined a service club.
176. My first corsage — and how it thrilled me.
177. I was embarrassed because I could not remember a name.
178. A picnic I will always remember.

Miscellaneous

179. A problem I helped solve at our office (factory, home, club, school).
180. I got a ticket for speeding.
181. Rain spoiled my plans.
182. The most interesting discussion I ever heard.
183. The best sermon I ever heard — and how it affected me.
184. The most tragic accident I ever saw.
185. I was in a foreign country.
186. The mental and emotional impact that this Course has had on me.
187. The day the war ended.
188. My favorite recipe.
189. Why I regret I never went to college (or university).
190. When persistence paid off.
191. I was provoked because someone was late for an appointment.
192. The last time I had a flat tire.
193. My first trip in a jet plane.
194. I had my fortune told.
195. The smartest "mistake" I ever made.
196. A storm I will never forget.
197. An incident that convinced me that "It is better to give than to receive."
198. An incident that convinced me that "Honesty is the best policy."
199. I ran out of gasoline.
200. Why I am taking this Course — and what I am getting out of it.

WINNERS OF THE PENCIL AWARDS

Session	Best Speech	Most Improvement	Special Award
2.			
3.			
4.			
5.			
7.			
8.			
9.			

AWARDS IN SESSION TWELVE

WINNERS OF THE BOOK AWARDS

Lincoln the Unknown

Don't Grow Old—Grow Up!

Dale Carnegie's Scrapbook

CHAMPIONS

Prepared Speech

Impromptu Speech

Highest Award for Achievement

ROSTER of CLASS NO.

ROSTER of CLASS NO._____

This book belongs to

_____

Name

_____

Address

_____

_____

Telephone

_____

Class

==

Names and addresses of friends who might be interested in joining a Dale Carnegie Class.

Name	Address

Your Name:

Address:

Class No.:

(To be filled in if we may use your name for reference)

**Names and addresses of friends who might be
interested in joining a Dale Carnegie Class.**

Name   Address

_____

_____

_____

_____

_____

_____

_____

_____

_____

_____

_____

_____

_____

_____

Names and addresses of friends who might be interested in joining a Dale Carnegie Class.

Name   Address

_____

_____

_____

_____

_____

_____

_____

_____

_____

_____

Your Name: _____

Address: _____

Class No.: _____

(To be filled in if we may use your name for reference)

**Names and addresses of friends who might be
interested in joining a Dale Carnegie Class.**

Name   Address

_____

_____

_____

_____

_____

_____

_____

_____

_____

_____

_____

_____

NOTES

NOTES

PRINTED IN U.S.A.